GOLF LOG
& RECORD

Editor: James Deen
Design & Typesetting: Jago Design Management
Printed in China

Golf Log & Record is published by Golf Log Media

USA	UK
1005 N. Commons Drive	Dept 449
Aurora	2 Lansdowne Row
Illinois 60504	London W1J 6HL
Tel (866) 693 3285	Tel 0870 005 3494

www.golflogrecord.com

ISBN: 0-86281-928-8

GOLF LOG
& RECORD

www.golflogrecord.com

GOLF CLUB INFORMATION

Golf Club (1) _____

Address _____

_____

_____

Membership No. _____

Telephone (Club) _____

Telephone (Pro) _____

Golf Club (2) _____

Address _____

_____

_____

Membership No. _____

Telephone (Club) _____

Telephone (Pro) _____

My handicap index tracker

JANUARY	FEBRUARY	MARCH	APRIL	MAY	JUNE

PERSONAL INFORMATION

Name _____

Address _____

_____

_____

Home Telephone _____

Mobile/Cellphone _____

Home Email _____

Business Address _____

_____

_____

Business Telephone _____

Fax _____

Business Email _____

In case of emergency
please contact _____

Telephone _____

JULY	AUGUST	SEPTEMBER	OCTOBER	NOVEMBER	DECEMBER

GOLF LOG
& RECORD

www.golflogrecord.com

WELCOME

Welcome to the updated *Golf Log & Record* - packed with new features and sections that I know will be of great use to you.

In this new edition you will find:-

- Lesson record
- Competition pages
- Club dimensions and distance charts
- A year planner
- Improved log and record pages with "up and downs"
- Pages for notes and practice drills

Used as a great tee gift or professional shop item, the *Golf Log & Record* has become the standard for recording the progress of your game whilst also having the benefit of logging your scores and naming your partners. It is great fun to look back on all the games that you have had over time.

We offer a full embossing and customised service as well as logs, record books and diaries for players of all standards and situations. Please check our website for the latest news and details of our sponsored professionals as they battle their way round the world's greatest tournaments with the world's greatest players. You can find us at **www.golflogrecord.com**.

Thank you for the correspondence and keep it coming! Happy golfing to you and your friends over the coming months!

James Deen

James Deen
Orlando

HOW TO USE THIS GOLF LOG

GOLF GAME LOG   Game No. _____ 6 _____   Date __ January 20th 2005 __

Course __ The Oaks __   Par __ 72 __   Tees used __ Blk __   Yardage __ 6,610 __   Time of Play __ 4.30 __

Players	Handicap	Gross	Net	Points
Me	12	91	79	
Michael Wright	14	88	74	
Stefan Browski	9	85	76	
David Williams	18	102	84	

Result in match __ Lost to MW __   Competition _____   Format ____ 4 Ball ____

		Course Rating	73.2
		Slope Rating	137

Game Rating

						Fun					
Driving	1	②	3	4	5	Short irons	1	②	3	4	5
Long irons	1	2	③	4	5	Chipping	1	2	③	4	5
Long putts	1	2	③	4	5	Short putts	1	2	3	④	5

Use / to denote Par 3 holes

	1	2	3	4	5	6	7	8	9	10	11	12	13	14	15	16	17	18	
Par	4	4	3	4	5	4	4	3	5	4	4	3	3	4	5	4	5	4	72
Score	6	5	4	6	5	6	4	5	6	4	5	5	4	5	7	5	5	4	91
Fairways hit	✓		/		✓		✓	/		✓	✓	/	/					✓	6 /14
Greens in Reg		✓			✓		✓		✓	✓	✓						✓	✓	7 /18
Putts	3	2	2	3	2	2	1	3	2	2	2	4	1	2	3	2	2	2	40
Up & Down								✓							✓				2

Eagles	—
Birdies	—
Pars	5
Bogeys	7
Penalties	6
Sand Saves	0 / 3

Green speed (Fast) Med Slow
Balls used Titleist Pro V1
Weather Good
Wind NE-moderate
Temperature 75°

Practice priorities
Putting and driving

GOLF GAME LOG   Game No. _____   Date _____

| Course _____ | Par _____ | Tees used _____ | Yardage _____ | Time of Play _____ |
| | | | | |

Players

	Handicap	Gross	Net	Points
_____	___	___	___	___
_____	___	___	___	___
_____	___	___	___	___
_____	___	___	___	___
_____	___	___	___	___

| Result in match _____ | Competition _____ | | Format _____ |

Game Rating

Driving	1	2	3	4	5	Short irons	1	2	3	4	5	Course Rating _____
Long irons	1	2	3	4	5	Chipping	1	2	3	4	5	Slope Rating _____
Long putts	1	2	3	4	5	Short putts	1	2	3	4	5	

	1	2	3	4	5	6	7	8	9	10	11	12	13	14	15	16	17	18	
Par																			
Score																			
Fairways hit																			
Greens in Reg																		18	
Putts																			
Up & Down																			

Green speed *Fast Med Slow*

Balls used _____
Weather _____
Wind _____
Temperature _____

Eagles _____
Birdies _____
Pars _____
Bogeys _____
Other _____
Sand Saves _____

Practice priorities

_____
_____
_____
_____

GOLF GAME LOG Game No. _____ Date _____

Course _____	Par _____	Tees used _____	Yardage _____	Time of Play _____

Players

		Handicap	Gross	Net	Points
_____	_____	_____	_____	_____	_____
_____	_____	_____	_____	_____	_____
_____	_____	_____	_____	_____	_____
_____	_____	_____	_____	_____	_____

Result in match _____	Competition _____	Format _____

Game Rating

										Course Rating _____
Driving	1	2	3	4	5	Short irons	1	2	3	4	5
Long irons	1	2	3	4	5	Chipping	1	2	3	4	5
Long putts	1	2	3	4	5	Short putts	1	2	3	4	5

Slope Rating _____

	1	2	3	4	5	6	7	8	9	10	11	12	13	14	15	16	17	18	
Par																			
Score																			
Fairways hit																			
Greens in Reg																			18
Putts																			
Up & Down																			

Green speed Fast Med Slow
Balls used _____
Weather _____
Wind _____
Temperature _____

Eagles _____
Birdies _____
Pars _____
Bogeys _____
Other _____
Sand Saves ___/___

Practice priorities
_____
_____
_____
_____

GOLF GAME LOG   Game No. _____   Date _____

Course _____   Par _____   Tees used _____   Yardage _____   Time of Play _____

Players	Handicap	Gross	Net	Points

Result in match _____   Competition _____   Format _____

Course Rating _____
Slope Rating _____

Game Rating

Driving	1	2	3	4	5	Short irons	1	2	3	4	5
Long irons	1	2	3	4	5	Chipping	1	2	3	4	5
Long putts	1	2	3	4	5	Short putts	1	2	3	4	5

	1	2	3	4	5	6	7	8	9	10	11	12	13	14	15	16	17	18	
Par																			
Score																			
Fairways hit																		/	
Greens in Reg																		/18	
Putts																			
Up & Down																			

Green speed *Fast Med Slow*

Balls used _____

Weather _____

Wind _____

Temperature _____

Eagles _____
Birdies _____
Pars _____
Bogeys _____
Other _____
Sand Saves ___/___

Practice priorities
_____
_____
_____

GOLF GAME LOG

Game No. _____ Date _____

| Course _____ | Par _____ | Tees used _____ | Yardage _____ | Time of Play _____ |

Players	Handicap	Gross	Net	Points
_____	___	___	___	___
_____	___	___	___	___
_____	___	___	___	___
_____	___	___	___	___

Result in match _____ Competition _____ Format _____

Game Rating

Driving	1	2	3	4	5	Short irons	1	2	3	4	5	Course Rating _____
Long irons	1	2	3	4	5	Chipping	1	2	3	4	5	
Long putts	1	2	3	4	5	Short putts	1	2	3	4	5	Slope Rating _____

	1	2	3	4	5	6	7	8	9	10	11	12	13	14	15	16	17	18	
Par																			
Score																			
Fairways hit																			
Greens in Reg																			18
Putts																			
Up & Down																			

Green speed *Fast Med Slow*

Balls used _____

Weather _____

Wind _____

Temperature _____

Eagles _____
Birdies _____
Pars _____
Bogeys _____
Other _____
Sand Saves _____/

Practice priorities
_____
_____
_____
_____

GOLF GAME LOG   Game No. _____   Date _____

Course _____   Par _____   Tees used _____   Yardage _____   Time of Play _____

Players		Handicap	Gross	Net	Points

Result in match _____   Competition _____   Format _____

Game Rating

Driving	1 2 3 4 5	Short irons	1 2 3 4 5	Course Rating _____
Long irons	1 2 3 4 5	Chipping	1 2 3 4 5	Slope Rating _____
Long putts	1 2 3 4 5	Short putts	1 2 3 4 5	

	1	2	3	4	5	6	7	8	9	10	11	12	13	14	15	16	17	18	
Par																			
Score																			
Fairways hit																			
Greens in Reg																		18	
Putts																			
Up & Down																			

Eagles _____
Birdies _____
Pars _____
Bogeys _____
Other _____
Sand Saves __/__

Green speed *Fast Med Slow*
Balls used _____
Weather _____
Wind _____
Temperature _____

Practice priorities
_____
_____
_____
_____

GOLF GAME LOG   Game No. _____   Date _____

Course _____   Par _____   Tees used _____   Yardage _____   Time of Play _____

Players		Handicap	Gross	Net	Points

Result in match _____   Competition _____   Format _____

Game Rating

Driving	1 2 3 4 5		Short irons	1 2 3 4 5		Course Rating _____
Long irons	1 2 3 4 5		Chipping	1 2 3 4 5		Slope Rating _____
Long putts	1 2 3 4 5		Short putts	1 2 3 4 5		

	1	2	3	4	5	6	7	8	9	10	11	12	13	14	15	16	17	18	
Par																			
Score																			
Fairways hit																		/	
Greens in Reg																		/ 18	
Putts																			
Up & Down																			

Green speed *Fast* *Med* *Slow*

Balls used ——————

Weather ——————

Wind ——————

Temperature ——————

Eagles ——————
Birdies ——————
Pars ——————
Bogeys ——————
Other ——————
Sand Saves ——/——

Practice priorities

——————
——————
——————
——————

GOLF GAME LOG   Game No. _____   Date _____

| Course _____ | Par _____ | Tees used _____ | Yardage _____ | Time of Play _____ |

Players

	Handicap	Gross	Net	Points

Result in match _____   Competition _____   Format _____

Game Rating

								Course Rating _____
Driving	1	2	3	4	5	Short irons	1 2 3 4 5	Course Rating _____
Long irons	1	2	3	4	5	Chipping	1 2 3 4 5	Slope Rating _____
Long putts	1	2	3	4	5	Short putts	1 2 3 4 5	

	1	2	3	4	5	6	7	8	9	10	11	12	13	14	15	16	17	18	
Par																			
Score																			
Fairways hit																			
Greens in Reg																			18
Putts																			
Up & Down																			

Green speed *Fast Med Slow*
Balls used _____
Weather _____
Wind _____
Temperature _____

Eagles _____
Birdies _____
Pars _____
Bogeys _____
Other _____
Sand Saves ____/____

Practice priorities
_____
_____
_____

GOLF GAME LOG

Game No. _____ Date _____

Course _____	Par _____	Tees used _____	Yardage _____	Time of Play _____

Players				Handicap	Gross	Net	Points
				___	___	___	___
				___	___	___	___
				___	___	___	___
				___	___	___	___
				___	___	___	___

Result in match _____	Competition _____	Format _____

Game Rating

Driving	1 2 3 4 5	Short irons	1 2 3 4 5	Course Rating _____
Long irons	1 2 3 4 5	Chipping	1 2 3 4 5	
Long putts	1 2 3 4 5	Short putts	1 2 3 4 5	Slope Rating _____

	1	2	3	4	5	6	7	8	9	10	11	12	13	14	15	16	17	18	
Par																			
Score																			
Fairways hit																			/
Greens in Reg																			/18
Putts																			
Up & Down																			

Green speed Fast Med Slow

Balls used _____

Weather _____

Wind _____

Temperature _____

Eagles _____

Birdies _____

Pars _____

Bogeys _____

Other _____

Sand Saves ____/____

Practice priorities

_____

_____

_____

GOLF GAME LOG   Game No. _____   Date _____

| Course _____ | Par _____ | Tees used _____ | Yardage _____ | Time of Play _____ |

Players

	Handicap	Gross	Net	Points
_____	_____	_____	_____	_____
_____	_____	_____	_____	_____
_____	_____	_____	_____	_____
_____	_____	_____	_____	_____
_____	_____	_____	_____	_____

Result in match _____   Competition _____   Format _____

Game Rating

			Course Rating _____
Driving	1 2 3 4 5	Short irons	1 2 3 4 5
Long irons	1 2 3 4 5	Chipping	1 2 3 4 5	Slope Rating _____
Long putts	1 2 3 4 5	Short putts	1 2 3 4 5

	1	2	3	4	5	6	7	8	9	10	11	12	13	14	15	16	17	18	
Par																			
Score																			
Fairways hit																			
Greens in Reg																			/18
Putts																			
Up & Down																			

Green speed *Fast Med Slow*
Balls used _____
Weather _____
Wind _____
Temperature _____

Eagles _____
Birdies _____
Pars _____
Bogeys _____
Other _____
Sand Saves ___/___

Practice priorities
_____
_____
_____
_____

GOLF GAME LOG Game No. _____ Date _____

Course _____ Par _____ Tees used _____ Yardage _____ Time of Play _____

Players		Handicap	Gross	Net	Points

Result in match _____ Competition _____ Format _____

Game Rating

Driving	1 2 3 4 5	Short irons	1 2 3 4 5	Course Rating	_____
Long irons	1 2 3 4 5	Chipping	1 2 3 4 5	Slope Rating	_____
Long putts	1 2 3 4 5	Short putts	1 2 3 4 5		

	1	2	3	4	5	6	7	8	9	10	11	12	13	14	15	16	17	18	
Par																			
Score																			
Fairways hit																			/
Greens in Reg																			/18
Putts																			
Up & Down																			

Green speed *Fast Med Slow*

Balls used _____

Weather _____

Wind _____

Temperature _____

Eagles _____
Birdies _____
Pars _____
Bogeys _____
Other _____
Sand Saves ____/____

Practice priorities
_____
_____
_____

GOLF GAME LOG   Game No. _____

Course _____   Par _____   Tees used _____   Yardage _____   Date _____

Players		Handicap	Gross	Net	Time of Play _____ Points
_____		___	___	___	___
_____		___	___	___	___
_____		___	___	___	___
_____		___	___	___	___
_____		___	___	___	___

Result in match _____   Competition _____   Format _____

Game Rating

Driving	1	2	3	4	5	Short irons	1	2	3	4	5
Long irons	1	2	3	4	5	Chipping	1	2	3	4	5
Long putts	1	2	3	4	5	Short putts	1	2	3	4	5

Course Rating _____
Slope Rating _____

	1	2	3	4	5	6	7	8	9	10	11	12	13	14	15	16	17	18	
Par																			
Score																			
Fairways hit																			
Greens in Reg																		18	
Putts																			
Up & Down																			

Green speed *Fast Med Slow*

Balls used _____

Weather _____

Wind _____

Temperature _____

Eagles _____
Birdies _____
Pars _____
Bogeys _____
Other _____
Sand Saves ___/___

Practice priorities
_____
_____
_____
_____

GOLF GAME LOG   Game No. _____   Date _____

Course _____	Par _____	Tees used _____	Yardage _____		Time of Play _____

Players	Handicap	Gross	Net	Points
	___	___	___	___
	___	___	___	___
	___	___	___	___
	___	___	___	___
	___	___	___	___

Result in match _____   Competition _____   Format _____

Game Rating

Driving	1 2 3 4 5	Short irons	1 2 3 4 5	Course Rating ___
Long irons	1 2 3 4 5	Chipping	1 2 3 4 5	
Long putts	1 2 3 4 5	Short putts	1 2 3 4 5	Slope Rating ___

	1	2	3	4	5	6	7	8	9	10									
Score																			
Fairways hit																			
Greens in Reg																			/18
Putts																			
Up & Down																			

Green speed *Fast Med Slow*

Balls used _____

Weather _____

Wind _____

Temperature _____

Eagles _____
Birdies _____
Pars _____
Bogeys _____
Other _____
Sand Saves ___/___

Practice priorities
_____
_____
_____

GOLF GAME LOG   Game No. _____   Date _____

Course _____   Par _____   Tees used _____   Yardage _____   Time of Play _____

Players

	Handicap	Gross	Net	Points
	___	___	___	___
	___	___	___	___
	___	___	___	___
	___	___	___	___
	___	___	___	___

Result in match _____   Competition _____   Format _____

Game Rating

Driving	1	2	3	4	5	Short irons	1	2	3	4	5	Course Rating ___
Long irons	1	2	3	4	5	Chipping	1	2	3	4	5	Slope Rating ___
Long putts	1	2	3	4	5	Short putts	1	2	3	4	5	

	1	2	3	4	5	6	7	8	9	10	11	12	13	14	15	16	17	18	
Par																			
Score																			
Fairways hit																		╱	
Greens in Reg																		╱18	
Putts																			
Up & Down																			

Green speed *Fast* *Med* *Slow*
Balls used _____
Weather _____
Wind _____
Temperature _____

Eagles _____
Birdies _____
Pars _____
Bogeys _____
Other _____
Sand Saves ____╱____

Practice priorities
_____
_____
_____

GOLF GAME LOG   Game No. _____   Date _____

| Course _____ | Par _____ | Tees used _____ | Yardage _____ | Time of Play _____ |

Players

	Handicap	Gross	Net	Points
	—	—	—	—
	—	—	—	—
	—	—	—	—
	—	—	—	—
	—	—	—	—

| Result in match _____ | Competition _____ | Format _____ |

Game Rating

Driving	1 2 3 4 5	Short irons	1 2 3 4 5	Course Rating _____
Long irons	1 2 3 4 5	Chipping	1 2 3 4 5	
Long putts	1 2 3 4 5	Short putts	1 2 3 4 5	Slope Rating _____

	1	2	3	4	5	6	7	8	9	10	11	12	13	14	15	16	17	18	
Par																			
Score																			
Fairways hit																			/
Greens in Reg																			/18
Putts																			
Up & Down																			

Green speed *Fast Med Slow*
Balls used _____
Weather _____
Wind _____
Temperature _____

Eagles _____
Birdies _____
Pars _____
Bogeys _____
Other _____
Sand Saves _____ /

Practice priorities
_____
_____
_____

GOLF GAME LOG   Game No. _____   Date _____

Course _____	Par _____	Tees used _____	Yardage _____	Time of Play _____

Players

	Handicap	Gross	Net	Points
_____	_____	_____	_____	_____
_____	_____	_____	_____	_____
_____	_____	_____	_____	_____
_____	_____	_____	_____	_____
_____	_____	_____	_____	_____

Result in match _____   Competition _____   Format _____

Game Rating

							Course Rating _____
Driving	1	2	3	4	5	Short irons	1 2 3 4 5
Long irons	1	2	3	4	5	Chipping	1 2 3 4 5	Course Rating _____
Long putts	1	2	3	4	5	Short putts	1 2 3 4 5	Slope Rating _____

	1	2	3	4	5	6	7	8	9	10	11	12	13	14	15	16	17	18	
Par																			
Score																			
Fairways hit																			/
Greens in Reg																			/18
Putts																			
Up & Down																			

Green speed Fast Med Slow
Balls used ____
Weather ____
Wind ____
Temperature ____

Eagles ____
Birdies ____
Pars ____
Bogeys ____
Other ____
Sand Saves ____ /

Practice priorities
____
____
____

GOLF GAME LOG   Game No. _____   Date _____

Course _____   Par _____   Tees used _____   Yardage _____   Time of Play _____

Players	Handicap	Gross	Net	Points

Result in match _____   Competition _____   Format _____

Game Rating

Driving	1	2	3	4	5	Short irons	1	2	3	4	5
Long irons	1	2	3	4	5	Chipping	1	2	3	4	5
Long putts	1	2	3	4	5	Short putts	1	2	3	4	5

Course Rating _____
Slope Rating _____

	1	2	3	4	5	6	7	8	9	10	11	12	13	14	15	16	17	18	
Par																			
Score																			
Fairways hit																			
Greens in Reg																			18
Putts																			
Up & Down																			

Green speed Fast Med Slow

Balls used _____

Weather _____

Wind _____

Temperature _____

Eagles _____
Birdies _____
Pars _____
Bogeys _____
Other _____
Sand Saves _____ / _____

Practice priorities
_____
_____
_____

GOLF GAME LOG   Game No. _____   Date _____

Course _____		Par _____	Tees used _____	Yardage _____			Time of Play _____
Players				Handicap	Gross	Net	Points
_____				_____	_____	_____	_____
_____				_____	_____	_____	_____
_____				_____	_____	_____	_____
_____				_____	_____	_____	_____

Result in match _____		Competition _____		Format _____		

Game Rating

Driving	1	2	3	4	5	Short irons	1	2	3	4	5	Course Rating _____
Long irons	1	2	3	4	5	Chipping	1	2	3	4	5	Slope Rating _____
Long putts	1	2	3	4	5	Short putts	1	2	3	4	5	

	1	2	3	4	5	6	7	8	9	10	11	12	13	14	15	16	17	18	
Par																			
Score																			
Fairways hit																		/	
Greens in Reg																		/18	
Putts																			
Up & Down																			

Green speed *Fast Med Slow*

Balls used _____

Weather _____

Wind _____

Temperature _____

Eagles _____
Birdies _____
Pars _____
Bogeys _____
Other _____
Sand Saves ____/____

Practice priorities

_____

_____

_____

GOLF GAME LOG   Game No. _____   Date _____

Course _____	Par _____	Tees used _____	Yardage _____	Time of Play _____

Players		Handicap	Gross	Net	Points
_____		___	___	___	___
_____		___	___	___	___
_____		___	___	___	___
_____		___	___	___	___
_____		___	___	___	___

Result in match _____	Competition _____	Format _____

Game Rating

Driving	1	2	3	4	5	Short irons	1 2 3 4 5	Course Rating ___
Long irons	1	2	3	4	5	Chipping	1 2 3 4 5	Slope Rating ___
Long putts	1	2	3	4	5	Short putts	1 2 3 4 5	

	1	2	3	4	5	6	7	8	9	10	11	12	13	14	15	16	17	18	
Par																			
Score																			
Fairways hit																			/
Greens in Reg																			/18
Putts																			
Up & Down																			

Practice priorities

_____

_____

_____

_____

Eagles	___
Birdies	___
Pars	___
Bogeys	___
Other	___
Sand Saves	/

Green speed *Fast* *Med* *Slow*

Balls used ___

Weather ___

Wind ___

Temperature ___

GOLF GAME LOG   Game No. _____   Date _____

Course _____	Par _____	Tees used _____	Yardage _____	Time of Play _____

Players

	Handicap	Gross	Net	Points
_____	_____	_____	_____	_____
_____	_____	_____	_____	_____
_____	_____	_____	_____	_____
_____	_____	_____	_____	_____
_____	_____	_____	_____	_____

Result in match _____	Competition _____	Format _____

			Course Rating _____
Short irons	1 2 3 4 5		
Chipping	1 2 3 4 5		Slope Rating _____
Short putts	1 2 3 4 5		

Game Rating

Driving	1 2 3 4 5
Long irons	1 2 3 4 5
Long putts	1 2 3 4 5

	1	2	3	4	5	6	7	8	9	10	11	12	13	14	15	16	17	18	
Par																			
Score																				
Fairways hit																				
Greens in Reg																				18
Putts																				
Up & Down																				

Green speed *Fast Med Slow*
Balls used ____
Weather ____
Wind ____
Temperature ____

Eagles ____
Birdies ____
Pars ____
Bogeys ____
Other ____
Sand Saves ____/____

Practice priorities
____
____
____

GOLF GAME LOG   Game No. _____   Date _____

Course _____   Par _____   Tees used _____   Yardage _____   Time of Play _____

Players

	Handicap	Gross	Net	Points
_____	_____	_____	_____	_____
_____	_____	_____	_____	_____
_____	_____	_____	_____	_____
_____	_____	_____	_____	_____

Result in match _____   Competition _____   Format _____

Game Rating

Driving	1	2	3	4	5	Short irons	1	2	3	4	5	Course Rating _____
Long irons	1	2	3	4	5	Chipping	1	2	3	4	5	Slope Rating _____
Long putts	1	2	3	4	5	Short putts	1	2	3	4	5	

	1	2	3	4	5	6	7	8	9	10	11	12	13	14	15	16	17	18	
Par																			
Score																			
Fairways hit																			/
Greens in Reg																			/18
Putts																			
Up & Down																			

Green speed	Fast	Med	Slow
Balls used	___		
Weather	___		
Wind	___		
Temperature	___		

Eagles	___
Birdies	___
Pars	___
Bogeys	___
Other	___
Sand Saves	__/__

Practice priorities

_____
_____
_____

GOLF GAME LOG Game No. _____ Date _____

Course _____ Par _____ Tees used _____ Yardage _____ Time of Play _____

Players	Handicap	Gross	Net	Points
_____	_____	_____	_____	_____
_____	_____	_____	_____	_____
_____	_____	_____	_____	_____
_____	_____	_____	_____	_____

Result in match _____ Competition _____ Format _____

				Short irons	1	2 3	4	5	Course Rating _____
				Chipping	1	2 3	4	5	Slope Rating _____
				Short putts	1	2 3	4	5	

Game Rating

Driving	1	2 3	4	5
Long irons	1	2 3	4	5
Long putts	1	2 3	4	5

	1	2	3	4	5	6	7	8	9	10	11	12	13	14	15	16	17	18	
Par																			
Score																			
Fairways hit																			/
Greens in Reg																			/18
Putts																			
Up & Down																			

Green speed *Fast Med Slow*

Balls used _____

Weather _____

Wind _____

Temperature _____

Eagles _____
Birdies _____
Pars _____
Bogeys _____
Other _____
Sand Saves _____ /

Practice priorities

_____

_____

_____

_____

GOLF GAME LOG   Game No. _____   Date _____

| Course _____ | Par _____ | Tees used _____ | Yardage _____ | Time of Play _____ |

Players

	Handicap	Gross	Net	Points
_____	____	____	____	____
_____	____	____	____	____
_____	____	____	____	____
_____	____	____	____	____
_____	____	____	____	____

| Result in match _____ | Competition _____ | Format _____ |

Game Rating

Driving	1	2	3	4	5	Short irons	1	2	3	4	5	Course Rating _____
Long irons	1	2	3	4	5	Chipping	1	2	3	4	5	
Long putts	1	2	3	4	5	Short putts	1	2	3	4	5	Slope Rating _____

	1	2	3	4	5	6	7	8	9	10	11	12	13	14	15	16	17	18	
Par																			
Score																			
Fairways hit																			
Greens in Reg																			/18
Putts																			
Up & Down																			

Green speed *Fast Med Slow*	
Balls used	_____
Weather	_____
Wind	_____
Temperature	_____

Eagles	_____
Birdies	_____
Pars	_____
Bogeys	_____
Other	_____
Sand Saves	___/___

Practice priorities

_____

_____

GOLF GAME LOG Game No. _____ Date _____

| Course _____ | Par _____ | Tees used _____ | Yardage _____ | Time of Play _____ |

Players

	Handicap	Gross	Net	Points
	___	___	___	___
	___	___	___	___
	___	___	___	___
	___	___	___	___
	___	___	___	___

| Result in match _____ | Competition _____ | Format _____ |

Short irons	1	2	3	4	5			Course Rating ___	
Chipping	1	2	3	4	5			Slope Rating ___	
Short putts	1	2	3	4	5				

Game Rating

Driving	1	2	3	4	5
Long irons	1	2	3	4	5
Long putts	1	2	3	4	5

	1	2	3	4	5	6	7	8	9	10	11	12	13	14	15	16	17	18	
Par																			
Score																			
Fairways hit																			
Greens in Reg																			18
Putts																			
Up & Down																			

Green speed Fast Med Slow
Balls used _____
Weather _____
Wind _____
Temperature _____

Eagles _____
Birdies _____
Pars _____
Bogeys _____
Other _____
Sand Saves _____

Practice priorities
_____
_____
_____
_____
_____

GOLF GAME LOG   Game No. _____   Date _____

Course _____	Par _____	Tees used _____	Yardage _____	Time of Play _____

Players

		Handicap	Gross	Net	Points
		——	——	——	——
		——	——	——	——
		——	——	——	——
		——	——	——	——

Result in match _____	Competition _____	Format _____

Game Rating

Driving	1 2 3 4 5	Short irons	1 2 3 4 5	Course Rating	——
Long irons	1 2 3 4 5	Chipping	1 2 3 4 5	Slope Rating	——
Long putts	1 2 3 4 5	Short putts	1 2 3 4 5		

	1	2	3	4	5	6	7	8	9	10	11	12	13	14	15	16	17	18	
Par																			
Score																			
Fairways hit																			
Greens in Reg																		18	
Putts																			
Up & Down																			

Green speed *Fast Med Slow*
Balls used _____
Weather _____
Wind _____
Temperature _____

Eagles _____
Birdies _____
Pars _____
Bogeys _____
Other _____
Sand Saves ___/___

Practice priorities
_____
_____
_____
_____

GOLF GAME LOG   Game No. _____   Date _____

Course _____   Par _____   Tees used _____   Yardage _____   Time of Play _____

Players

	Handicap	Gross	Net	Points
	—	—	—	—
	—	—	—	—
	—	—	—	—
	—	—	—	—
	—	—	—	—

Result in match _____   Competition _____   Format _____

Game Rating

Driving	1 2 3 4 5	Short irons	1 2 3 4 5	Course Rating	—
Long irons	1 2 3 4 5	Chipping	1 2 3 4 5	Slope Rating	—
Long putts	1 2 3 4 5	Short putts	1 2 3 4 5		

	1	2	3	4	5	6	7	8	9	10	11	12	13	14	15	16	17	18	
Par																			
Score																			
Fairways hit																		/	
Greens in Reg																		/18	
Putts																			
Up & Down																			

Green speed	Fast	Med	Slow
Balls used	_____		
Weather	_____		
Wind	_____		
Temperature	_____		

Eagles _____
Birdies _____
Pars _____
Bogeys _____
Other _____
Sand Saves ___/___

Practice priorities
_____
_____
_____

GOLF GAME LOG   Game No. _____   Date _____

Course _____	Par _____	Tees used _____	Yardage _____	Time of Play _____

Players

		Handicap	Gross	Net	Points
___	___	___	___	___	___
___	___	___	___	___	___
___	___	___	___	___	___
___	___	___	___	___	___

Result in match _____	Competition _____	Format _____

Game Rating

Driving	1	2	3	4	5	Short irons	1	2	3	4	5
Long irons	1	2	3	4	5	Chipping	1	2	3	4	5
Long putts	1	2	3	4	5	Short putts	1	2	3	4	5

Course Rating _____
Slope Rating _____

	1	2	3	4	5	6	7	8	9	10	11	12	13	14	15	16	17	18	
Par																			
Score																			
Fairways hit																			/
Greens in Reg																			/18
Putts																			
Up & Down																			

Green speed *Fast Med Slow*

Balls used _____

Weather _____

Wind _____

Temperature _____

Eagles _____
Birdies _____
Pars _____
Bogeys _____
Other _____
Sand Saves ____/____

Practice priorities

_____

_____

_____

GOLF GAME LOG   Game No. _____   Date _____

| Course _____ | Par _____ | Tees used _____ | Yardage _____ | Time of Play _____ |

Players		Handicap	Gross	Net	Points
_____	_____	___	___	___	___
_____	_____	___	___	___	___
_____	_____	___	___	___	___
_____	_____	___	___	___	___

Result in match _____   Competition _____   Format _____

Game Rating										
Driving	1 2 3 4 5	Short irons	1 2 3 4 5	Course Rating _____
Long irons	1 2 3 4 5	Chipping	1 2 3 4 5	Slope Rating _____
Long putts	1 2 3 4 5	Short putts	1 2 3 4 5	

	1	2	3	4	5	6	7	8	9	10	11	12	13	14	15	16	17	18	
Par																			
Score																				
Fairways hit																			/
Greens in Reg																			/18
Putts																			
Up & Down																			

Green speed *Fast Med Slow*

Balls used _____

Weather _____

Wind _____

Temperature _____

Eagles _____
Birdies _____
Pars _____
Bogeys _____
Other _____
Sand Saves ____/____

Practice priorities

_____

_____

_____

GOLF GAME LOG   Game No. _____   Date _____

Course _____	Par _____	Tees used _____	Yardage _____	Time of Play _____

Players

	Handicap	Gross	Net	Points
_____	_____	_____	_____	_____
_____	_____	_____	_____	_____
_____	_____	_____	_____	_____
_____	_____	_____	_____	_____

Result in match _____   Competition _____   Format _____

					Course Rating _____
Short irons	1	2	3	4	5
Chipping	1	2	3	4	5	Slope Rating _____
Short putts	1	2	3	4	5

Game Rating

Driving	1	2	3	4	5
Long irons	1	2	3	4	5
Long putts	1	2	3	4	5

	1	2	3	4	5	6	7	8	9	10	11	12	13	14	15	16	17	18	
Par																			
Score																			
Fairways hit																			
Greens in Reg																		18	
Putts																			
Up & Down																			

Green speed *Fast Med Slow*
Balls used _____
Weather _____
Wind _____
Temperature _____

Eagles _____
Birdies _____
Pars _____
Bogeys _____
Other _____
Sand Saves _____ /

Practice priorities
_____
_____
_____
_____

GOLF GAME LOG   Game No. _____   Date _____

| Course _____ | Par _____ | Tees used _____ | Yardage _____ | Time of Play _____ |

Players	Handicap	Gross	Net	Points

| Result in match _____ | Competition _____ | Format _____ |

Game Rating

Driving	1 2 3 4 5	Short irons	1 2 3 4 5	Course Rating _____
Long irons	1 2 3 4 5	Chipping	1 2 3 4 5	Slope Rating _____
Long putts	1 2 3 4 5	Short putts	1 2 3 4 5	

	1	2	3	4	5	6	7	8	9	10	11	12	13	14	15	16	17	18	
Par																			
Score																			
Fairways hit																			/
Greens in Reg																			/18
Putts																			
Up & Down																			

Green speed *Fast Med Slow*

Balls used ____
Weather ____
Wind ____
Temperature ____

Eagles ____
Birdies ____
Pars ____
Bogeys ____
Other ____
Sand Saves ____ /

Practice priorities

____
____
____

GOLF GAME LOG Game No. _____ Date _____

Course _____	Par _____	Tees used _____	Yardage _____	Time of Play _____		

Players	Handicap	Gross	Net	Points
_____	___	___	___	___
_____	___	___	___	___
_____	___	___	___	___
_____	___	___	___	___

Result in match _____	Competition _____	Format _____

Game Rating

Driving	1 2 3 4 5	Short irons	1 2 3 4 5	Course Rating _____
Long irons	1 2 3 4 5	Chipping	1 2 3 4 5	
Long putts	1 2 3 4 5	Short putts	1 2 3 4 5	Slope Rating _____

	1	2	3	4	5	6	7	8	9	10	11	12	13	14	15	16	17	18		
Par																				
Score																				
Fairways hit																			/	
Greens in Reg																			/18	
Putts																				
Up & Down																				

Green speed	Fast	Med	Slow
Balls used	___		
Weather	___		
Wind	___		
Temperature	___		

Eagles	___
Birdies	___
Pars	___
Bogeys	___
Other	___
Sand Saves	___ / ___

Practice priorities

___
___
___
___

GOLF GAME LOG   Game No. _____   Date _____

Course _____   Par _____   Tees used _____   Yardage _____   Time of Play _____

Players

	Handicap	Gross	Net	Points
	—	—	—	—
	—	—	—	—
	—	—	—	—
	—	—	—	—
	—	—	—	—

Result in match _____   Competition _____   Format _____

Game Rating

Driving	1	2	3	4	5	Short irons	1	2	3	4	5	Course Rating _____
Long irons	1	2	3	4	5	Chipping	1	2	3	4	5	
Long putts	1	2	3	4	5	Short putts	1	2	3	4	5	Slope Rating _____

	1	2	3	4	5	6	7	8	9	10	11	12	13	14	15	16	17	18	
Par																			
Score																			
Fairways hit																			/
Greens in Reg																			/18
Putts																			
Up & Down																			

Green speed Fast Med Slow

Balls used ——————

Weather ——————

Wind ——————

Temperature ——————

Eagles ——————
Birdies ——————
Pars ——————
Bogeys ——————
Other ——————
Sand Saves ——/——

Practice priorities

——————

——————

——————

GOLF GAME LOG   Game No. _____   Date _____

Course _____   Par _____   Tees used _____   Yardage _____   Time of Play _____

Players				Handicap	Gross	Net	Points
				——	——	——	——
				——	——	——	——
				——	——	——	——
				——	——	——	——
				——	——	——	——

Result in match _____   Competition _____   Format _____

Game Rating

						Course Rating _____
Driving	1	2	3	4	5	Short irons	1	2	3	4	5
Long irons	1	2	3	4	5	Chipping	1	2	3	4	5	Slope Rating _____
Long putts	1	2	3	4	5	Short putts	1	2	3	4	5

	1	2	3	4	5	6	7	8	9	10	11	12	13	14	15	16	17	18	
Par																			
Score																			
Fairways hit																		/	
Greens in Reg																		/18	
Putts																			
Up & Down																			

Green speed *Fast Med Slow*

Balls used _____

Weather _____

Wind _____

Temperature _____

Eagles _____
Birdies _____
Pars _____
Bogeys _____
Other _____
Sand Saves ___/___

Practice priorities
_____
_____
_____
_____

GOLF GAME LOG Game No. _____ Date _____

| Course _____ | Par _____ | Tees used _____ | Yardage _____ | Time of Play _____ |

Players

	Handicap	Gross	Net	Points

Result in match _____ Competition _____ Format _____

Game Rating

Driving	1 2 3 4 5	Short irons	1 2 3 4 5	Course Rating	_____
Long irons	1 2 3 4 5	Chipping	1 2 3 4 5	Slope Rating	_____
Long putts	1 2 3 4 5	Short putts	1 2 3 4 5		

	1	2	3	4	5	6	7	8	9	10	11	12	13	14	15	16	17	18	
Par																			
Score																			
Fairways hit																			/
Greens in Reg																			/18
Putts																			
Up & Down																			

Green speed *Fast Med Slow*
Balls used _____
Weather _____
Wind _____
Temperature _____

Eagles _____
Birdies _____
Pars _____
Bogeys _____
Other _____
Sand Saves _____/_____

Practice priorities
_____
_____
_____

GOLF GAME LOG Game No. _____ Date _____

Course _____ Par _____ Tees used _____ Yardage _____ Time of Play _____

Players		Handicap	Gross	Net	Points
_____	_____	___	___	___	___
_____	_____	___	___	___	___
_____	_____	___	___	___	___
_____	_____	___	___	___	___
_____	_____	___	___	___	___

Result in match _____ Competition _____ Format _____

Game Rating

Driving	1	2	3	4	5	Short irons	1	2	3	4	5	Course Rating _____
Long irons	1	2	3	4	5	Chipping	1	2	3	4	5	Slope Rating _____
Long putts	1	2	3	4	5	Short putts	1	2	3	4	5	

	1	2	3	4	5	6	7	8	9	10	11	12	13	14	15	16	17	18	
Par																			
Score																			
Fairways hit																			/
Greens in Reg																			/18
Putts																			
Up & Down																			

Green speed *Fast* *Med* *Slow*

Balls used _____

Weather _____

Wind _____

Temperature _____

Eagles _____

Birdies _____

Pars _____

Bogeys _____

Other _____

Sand Saves ___/___

Practice priorities

_____

_____

_____

_____

GOLF GAME LOG   Game No. _____   Date _____

Course _____	Par _____	Tees used _____	Yardage _____		Time of Play _____	

Players

	Handicap	Gross	Net	Points
_____				
_____				
_____				
_____				
_____				

Result in match _____	Competition _____	Format _____

Game Rating

						Short irons	1	2	3	4	5	Course Rating _____
Driving	1	2	3	4	5	Chipping	1	2	3	4	5	Slope Rating _____
Long irons	1	2	3	4	5	Short putts	1	2	3	4	5	
Long putts	1	2	3	4	5							

	1	2	3	4	5	6	7	8	9	10	11	12	13	14	15	16	17	18	
Par																			
Score																				
Fairways hit																				
Greens in Reg																				18
Putts																				
Up & Down																				

Green speed *Fast Med Slow* ____
Balls used ____
Weather ____
Wind ____
Temperature ____

Eagles ____
Birdies ____
Pars ____
Bogeys ____
Other ____
Sand Saves ____

Practice priorities

____
____
____
____

GOLF GAME LOG   Game No. _____   Date _____

Course _____   Par _____   Tees used _____   Yardage _____   Time of Play _____

Players		Handicap	Gross	Net	Points
		___	___	___	___
		___	___	___	___
		___	___	___	___
		___	___	___	___
		___	___	___	___

Result in match _____   Competition _____   Format _____

Game Rating

Driving	1	2	3	4	5	Short irons	1	2	3	4	5	Course Rating ___
Long irons	1	2	3	4	5	Chipping	1	2	3	4	5	Slope Rating ___
Long putts	1	2	3	4	5	Short putts	1	2	3	4	5	

	1	2	3	4	5	6	7	8	9	10	11	12	13	14	15	16	17	18	
Par																			
Score																			
Fairways hit																			/
Greens in Reg																			/18
Putts																			
Up & Down																			

Green speed *Fast Med Slow*

Balls used _____

Weather _____

Wind _____

Temperature _____

Eagles _____
Birdies _____
Pars _____
Bogeys _____
Other _____
Sand Saves ___/___

Practice priorities
_____
_____
_____

GOLF GAME LOG   Game No. _____   Date _____

Course _____   Par _____   Tees used _____   Yardage _____   Time of Play _____

Players					Handicap	Gross	Net	Points
					___	___	___	___
					___	___	___	___
					___	___	___	___
					___	___	___	___
					___	___	___	___

Result in match _____   Competition _____   Format _____

Game Rating

Driving	1	2	3	4	5	Short irons	1	2	3	4	5	Course Rating ___
Long irons	1	2	3	4	5	Chipping	1	2	3	4	5	Slope Rating ___
Long putts	1	2	3	4	5	Short putts	1	2	3	4	5	

	1	2	3	4	5	6	7	8	9	10	11	12	13	14	15	16	17	18	
Par																			
Score																			
Fairways hit																			
Greens in Reg																		/18	
Putts																			
Up & Down																			

Green speed *Fast* *Med* *Slow*

Eagles	———
Birdies	———
Pars	———
Bogeys	———
Other	———
Sand Saves	——/—

Balls used ———
Weather ———
Wind ———
Temperature ———

Practice priorities

———————————
———————————
———————————

GOLF GAME LOG   Game No. _____   Date _____

Course _____   Par _____   Tees used _____   Yardage _____   Time of Play _____

Players

	Handicap	Gross	Net	Points
_____	_____	___	___	___
_____	_____	___	___	___
_____	_____	___	___	___
_____	_____	___	___	___

Result in match _____   Competition _____   Format _____

Game Rating

Driving	1	2	3	4	5	Short irons	1	2	3	4	5
Long irons	1	2	3	4	5	Chipping	1	2	3	4	5
Long putts	1	2	3	4	5	Short putts	1	2	3	4	5

Course Rating _____
Slope Rating _____

	1	2	3	4	5	6	7	8	9	10	11	12	13	14	15	16	17	18	
Par																			
Score																			
Fairways hit																		/	
Greens in Reg																		/18	
Putts																			
Up & Down																			

Green speed	Fast	Med	Slow
Balls used	_____		
Weather	_____		
Wind	_____		
Temperature	_____		

Eagles _____
Birdies _____
Pars _____
Bogeys _____
Other _____
Sand Saves ____/____

Practice priorities

_____
_____
_____

GOLF GAME LOG Game No. _____ Date _____

| Course _____ | Par _____ | Tees used _____ | Yardage _____ | Time of Play _____ |

Players

	Handicap	Gross	Net	Points
_____	___	___	___	___
_____	___	___	___	___
_____	___	___	___	___
_____	___	___	___	___
_____	___	___	___	___

| Result in match _____ | Competition _____ | Format _____ |

Game Rating

Driving	1	2	3	4	5	Short irons	1	2	3	4	5	Course Rating ___
Long irons	1	2	3	4	5	Chipping	1	2	3	4	5	Slope Rating ___
Long putts	1	2	3	4	5	Short putts	1	2	3	4	5	

	1	2	3	4	5	6	7	8	9	10	11	12	13	14	15	16	17	18	
Par																			
Score																			
Fairways hit																			
Greens in Reg																			/18
Putts																			
Up & Down																			

Green speed Fast Med Slow

Balls used _____

Weather _____

Wind _____

Temperature _____

Eagles _____
Birdies _____
Pars _____
Bogeys _____
Other _____
Sand Saves ___/___

Practice priorities
_____
_____
_____
_____

GOLF GAME LOG · Game No. _____ Date _____

Course _____ **Par** _____ **Tees used** _____ **Yardage** _____ **Time of Play** _____

Players

	Handicap	Gross	Net	Points
	___	___	___	___
	___	___	___	___
	___	___	___	___
	___	___	___	___

Result in match _____ **Competition** _____ **Format** _____

Game Rating

Driving	1	2	3	4	5	Short irons	1	2	3	4	5	Course Rating	___
Long irons	1	2	3	4	5	Chipping	1	2	3	4	5	Slope Rating	___
Long putts	1	2	3	4	5	Short putts	1	2	3	4	5		

	1	2	3	4	5	6	7	8	9	10	11	12	13	14	15	16	17	18	
Par																			
Score																			
Fairways hit																			/
Greens in Reg																			/18
Putts																			
Up & Down																			

Green speed *Fast Med Slow*
Balls used _____
Weather _____
Wind _____
Temperature _____

Eagles _____
Birdies _____
Pars _____
Bogeys _____
Other _____
Sand Saves _____ /

Practice priorities
_____
_____
_____

GOLF GAME LOG   Game No. _____   Date _____

Course _____	Par _____	Tees used _____	Yardage _____	Time of Play _____

Players	Handicap	Gross	Net	Points

Result in match	Competition _____	Format _____

Game Rating

Driving	1	2	3	4	5	Short irons	1	2	3	4	5	Course Rating _____
Long irons	1	2	3	4	5	Chipping	1	2	3	4	5	Slope Rating _____
Long putts	1	2	3	4	5	Short putts	1	2	3	4	5	

	1	2	3	4	5	6	7	8	9	10	11	12	13	14	15	16	17	18	
Par																			
Score																			
Fairways hit																			
Greens in Reg																			18
Putts																			
Up & Down																			

Green speed *Fast Med Slow*

Balls used _____

Weather _____

Wind _____

Temperature _____

Eagles _____
Birdies _____
Pars _____
Bogeys _____
Other _____
Sand Saves ____ / ____

Practice priorities
_____
_____
_____
_____

GOLF GAME LOG   Game No. _____   Date _____

| Course _____ | Par _____ | Tees used _____ | Yardage _____ | Time of Play _____ |

Players

	Handicap	Gross	Net	Points
_____	_____	_____	_____	_____
_____	_____	_____	_____	_____
_____	_____	_____	_____	_____
_____	_____	_____	_____	_____

Result in match _____   Competition _____   Format _____

Game Rating

Driving	1	2	3	4	5	Short irons	1	2	3	4	5	Course Rating _____
Long irons	1	2	3	4	5	Chipping	1	2	3	4	5	Slope Rating _____
Long putts	1	2	3	4	5	Short putts	1	2	3	4	5	

	1	2	3	4	5	6	7	8	9	10	11	12	13	14	15	16	17	18	
Par																			
Score																			
Fairways hit																			/
Greens in Reg																			/18
Putts																			
Up & Down																			

Eagles ——
Birdies ——
Pars ——
Bogeys ——
Other ——
Sand Saves ——/——

Green speed Fast Med Slow
Balls used ——
Weather ——
Wind ——
Temperature ——

Practice priorities
————————
————————
————————
————————

GOLF GAME LOG   Game No. _____   Date _____

Course _____   Par _____   Tees used _____   Yardage _____   Time of Play _____

Players			Handicap	Gross	Net	Points
_____			___	___	___	___
_____			___	___	___	___
_____			___	___	___	___
_____			___	___	___	___

Result in match _____   Competition _____   Format _____

Game Rating

			Course Rating ___
Driving	1 2 3 4 5	Short irons	1 2 3 4 5
Long irons	1 2 3 4 5	Chipping	1 2 3 4 5
Long putts	1 2 3 4 5	Short putts	1 2 3 4 5

Course Rating ___   Slope Rating ___

	1	2	3	4	5	6	7	8	9	10	11	12	13	14	15	16	17	18	
Par																			
Score																				
Fairways hit																			/	
Greens in Reg																		/18	
Putts																			
Up & Down																			

Green speed *Fast Med Slow*

Balls used _____

Weather _____

Wind _____

Temperature _____

Eagles _____
Birdies _____
Pars _____
Bogeys _____
Other _____
Sand Saves ___/___

Practice priorities

_____

_____

_____

GOLF GAME LOG   Game No. _____

Date _____

Course _____   Par _____   Tees used _____   Yardage _____   Time of Play _____

Players

	Handicap	Gross	Net	Points
_____	____	____	____	____
_____	____	____	____	____
_____	____	____	____	____
_____	____	____	____	____
_____	____	____	____	____

Result in match _____   Competition _____   Format _____

Game Rating

													Course Rating ____
Driving	1	2	3	4	5	Short irons	1	2	3	4	5		
Long irons	1	2	3	4	5	Chipping	1	2	3	4	5		Slope Rating ____
Long putts	1	2	3	4	5	Short putts	1	2	3	4	5		

	1	2	3	4	5	6	7	8	9	10	11	12	13	14	15	16	17	18	
Par																			
Score																				
Fairways hit																				/
Greens in Reg																				/18
Putts																				
Up & Down																				

Green speed _Fast_ _Med_ _Slow_

Balls used _____
Weather _____
Wind _____
Temperature _____

Eagles _____
Birdies _____
Pars _____
Bogeys _____
Other _____
Sand Saves ___/___

Practice priorities
_____
_____
_____
_____

GOLF GAME LOG

Game No. _____ Date _____

Course _____ Par _____ Tees used _____ Yardage _____ Time of Play _____

Players

	Handicap	Gross	Net	Points

Result in match _____ Competition _____ Format _____

Game Rating							
Driving	1	2	3	4	5	Short irons	1 2 3 4 5
Long irons	1	2	3	4	5	Chipping	1 2 3 4 5
Long putts	1	2	3	4	5	Short putts	1 2 3 4 5

Course Rating _____
Slope Rating _____

	1	2	3	4	5	6	7	8	9	10	11	12	13	14	15	16	17	18	
Par																			
Score																			
Fairways hit																			/
Greens in Reg																			/18
Putts																			
Up & Down																			

Green speed Fast Med Slow

Balls used _____

Weather _____

Wind _____

Temperature _____

Eagles _____
Birdies _____
Pars _____
Bogeys _____
Other _____
Sand Saves ____/____

Practice priorities

_____

_____

_____

GOLF GAME LOG   Game No. _____   Date _____

Course _____ Par _____ Tees used _____ Yardage _____ Time of Play _____

Players	Handicap	Gross	Net	Points
	____	____	____	____
	____	____	____	____
	____	____	____	____
	____	____	____	____
	____	____	____	____

Result in match _____ Competition _____ Format _____

Game Rating

Driving	1	2	3	4	5	Short irons	1	2	3	4	5	Course Rating ____
Long irons	1	2	3	4	5	Chipping	1	2	3	4	5	Slope Rating ____
Long putts	1	2	3	4	5	Short putts	1	2	3	4	5	

	1	2	3	4	5	6	7	8	9	10	11	12	13	14	15	16	17	18	
Par																			
Score																			
Fairways hit																			
Greens in Reg																			18
Putts																			
Up & Down																			

Green speed *Fast Med Slow*

Balls used —————

Weather —————

Wind —————

Temperature —————

Eagles —————
Birdies —————
Pars —————
Bogeys —————
Other —————
Sand Saves ——/——

Practice priorities

—————

—————

—————

—————

GOLF GAME LOG   Game No. _____   Date _____

| Course _____ | Par _____ | Tees used _____ | Yardage _____ | Time of Play _____ |

Players

	Handicap	Gross	Net	Points
_____	___	___	___	___
_____	___	___	___	___
_____	___	___	___	___
_____	___	___	___	___

| Result in match _____ | Competition _____ | Format _____ |

Game Rating

								Course Rating _____
Driving	1	2	3	4	5	Short irons	1 2 3 4 5	
Long irons	1	2	3	4	5	Chipping	1 2 3 4 5	Slope Rating _____
Long putts	1	2	3	4	5	Short putts	1 2 3 4 5	

	1	2	3	4	5	6	7	8	9	10	11	12	13	14	15	16	17	18	
Par																			
Score																				
Fairways hit																				
Greens in Reg																			18	
Putts																				
Up & Down																				

Green speed *Fast Med Slow*
Balls used _____
Weather _____
Wind _____
Temperature _____

Eagles _____
Birdies _____
Pars _____
Bogeys _____
Other _____
Sand Saves ___/___

Practice priorities
_____
_____
_____
_____

GOLF GAME LOG Game No. _____ Date _____

Course _____ Par _____ Tees used _____ Yardage _____ Time of Play _____

Players

	Handicap	Gross	Net	Points
	—	—	—	—
	—	—	—	—
	—	—	—	—
	—	—	—	—

Competition _____ Format _____

Result in match _____

Game Rating

Driving	1	2	3	4	5	Short irons	1	2	3	4	5	Course Rating _____
Long irons	1	2	3	4	5	Chipping	1	2	3	4	5	Slope Rating _____
Long putts	1	2	3	4	5	Short putts	1	2	3	4	5	

	1	2	3	4	5	6	7	8	9	10	11	12	13	14	15	16	17	18	
Par																			
Score																			
Fairways hit																			
Greens in Reg																			18
Putts																			
Up & Down																			

Green speed	Fast	Med	Slow
Balls used			
Weather			
Wind			
Temperature			

Eagles	
Birdies	
Pars	
Bogeys	
Other	
Sand Saves	/

Practice priorities
_____
_____
_____
_____
_____

GOLF GAME LOG   Game No. _____   Date _____

Course _____   Par _____   Tees used _____   Yardage _____   Time of Play _____

Players		Handicap	Gross	Net	Points
_____					
_____					
_____					
_____					
_____					
_____					

Result in match _____   Competition _____   Format _____

Game Rating

Driving	1	2	3	4	5	Short irons	1	2	3	4	5
Long irons	1	2	3	4	5	Chipping	1	2	3	4	5
Long putts	1	2	3	4	5	Short putts	1	2	3	4	5

Course Rating _____
Slope Rating _____

	1	2	3	4	5	6	7	8	9	10	11	12	13	14	15	16	17	18	
Par																			
Score																			
Fairways hit																			/
Greens in Reg																			/18
Putts																			
Up & Down																			

Green speed	Fast	Med	Slow
Balls used			
Weather			
Wind			
Temperature			

Eagles _____
Birdies _____
Pars _____
Bogeys _____
Other _____
Sand Saves ___/___

Practice priorities

_____
_____
_____
_____

GOLF GAME LOG   Game No. _____   Date _____

Course _____   Par _____   Tees used _____   Yardage _____   Time of Play _____

Players

	Handicap	Gross	Net	Points
_____	___	___	___	___
_____	___	___	___	___
_____	___	___	___	___
_____	___	___	___	___
_____	___	___	___	___
_____	___	___	___	___

Result in match _____   Competition _____   Format _____

Game Rating

Driving	1	2	3	4	5	Short irons	1	2	3	4	5
Long irons	1	2	3	4	5	Chipping	1	2	3	4	5
Long putts	1	2	3	4	5	Short putts	1	2	3	4	5

Course Rating _____   Slope Rating _____

	1	2	3	4	5	6	7	8	9	10	11	12	13	14	15	16	17	18	
Par																			
Score																			
Fairways hit																			
Greens in Reg																		18	
Putts																			
Up & Down																			

Green speed Fast Med Slow

Balls used ——————
Weather ——————
Wind ——————
Temperature ——————

Eagles ——————
Birdies ——————
Pars ——————
Bogeys ——————
Other ——————
Sand Saves ——————

Practice priorities
——————————
——————————
——————————
——————————

CLUB DIMENSIONS & RANGE

Club	Make	Loft	Lie	Length	1	2	3
Driver	___	___	___	___			
3 wood	___	___	___	___			
4 wood	___	___	___	___			
5 wood	___	___	___	___			
_ wood	___	___	___	___			
Utility							
1	___	___	___	___			
2	___	___	___	___			
Irons							
1	___	___	___	___			
2	___	___	___	___			
3	___	___	___	___			
4	___	___	___	___			

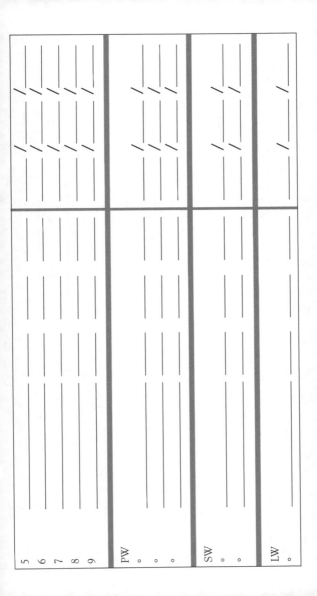

LESSON LOG

Date _____ Location _____ Teacher _____

Faults _____

_____

Fix _____

Drills _____

_____

_____

Date _____ Location _____ Teacher _____

Faults _____

_____

Fix _____

Drills _____

_____

_____

Date _____ Location _____ Teacher _____

Faults _____ Fix _____

Drills _____

_____

_____

Date _____ Location _____ Teacher _____

Faults _____ Fix _____

Drills _____

_____

_____

Remember!

LESSON LOG

Date _____ Location _____ Teacher _____

Faults _____

Fix _____

Drills _____

_____

Date _____ Location _____ Teacher _____

Faults _____

Fix _____

Drills _____

_____

Date _____ Location _____ Teacher _____

Faults _____ Fix _____

Drills _____

Date _____ Location _____ Teacher _____

Faults _____ Fix _____

Drills _____

Remember!

LESSON LOG

Date _____ Location _____ Teacher _____

Faults _____ Fix _____

Drills _____

_____

_____

_____

Date _____ Location _____ Teacher _____

Faults _____ Fix _____

Drills _____

_____

_____

_____

Date _____ Location _____ Teacher _____

Faults _____

_____ Fix _____

Drills _____

_____

_____

Date _____ Location _____ Teacher _____

Faults _____

_____ Fix _____

Drills _____

_____

_____

Remember!

LESSON LOG

Date	Location	Teacher
Faults		Fix
Drills		

Date	Location	Teacher
Faults		Fix
Drills		

Date	Location	Teacher
Faults		Fix
Drills		

Date	Location	Teacher
Faults		Fix
Drills		

Remember!

LESSON LOG

Date _____ Location _____ Teacher _____

Faults _____ Fix _____

Drills _____

_____

Date _____ Location _____ Teacher _____

Faults _____ Fix _____

Drills _____

Date _____ Location _____ Teacher _____

Faults _____

_____ Fix _____

Drills _____

_____

_____

Date _____ Location _____ Teacher _____

Faults _____

_____ Fix _____

Drills _____

_____

_____

Remember!

LESSON LOG

Date _____ Location _____ Teacher _____

Faults _____ Fix _____

Drills _____

_____

_____

Date _____ Location _____ Teacher _____

Faults _____ Fix _____

Drills _____

_____

_____

Date _____ Location _____ Teacher _____

Faults _____

_____ Fix _____

Drills _____

_____

_____

Date _____ Location _____ Teacher _____

Faults _____

_____ Fix _____

Drills _____

_____

_____

Remember!

PRACTICE NOTES

Date	Comments

Date	Comments

PRACTICE NOTES

Date	Comments

Date	Comments

PRACTICE NOTES

Date	Comments

Date	Comments

PRACTICE NOTES

Date	Comments

Date	Comments

PRACTICE NOTES

Date	Comments

Date	Comments

GOLF GAME SUMMARY

Game No.	Scores		Percentage			Putts	Per Green
	Gross	Net		Fairways	Greens		
Example: 13	83	72		7/14 50%	11/18 61%	36	2

| Game No. | Scores | | Percentage | | | | Per Green |
	Gross	Net	Fairways	Greens	Putts	

GOLF GAME SUMMARY

Game No.	Scores		Percentage			
	Gross	Net	Fairways	Greens	Putts	Per Green

| Game No. | Scores | | Percentage | | | |
	Gross	Net	Fairways	Greens	Putts	Per Green

GOLF GAME SUMMARY

Game No.	Scores		Percentage				
	Gross	Net	Fairways	Greens	Putts	Per Green

| Game No. | Scores | | Percentage | | | |
	Gross	Net	Fairways	Greens	Putts	Per Green

COMPETITIONS

Date	Tournament	Scores		Result
		Round 1	Round 2	

Date	Tournament	Scores		Result
		Round 1	Round 2	

GOLF CONTACTS

Name	Telephone/Email

Name	Telephone/Email

GOLF CONTACTS

Name	Telephone/Email

Name	Telephone/Email

GOLF CONTACTS

Name	Telephone/Email

Name		Telephone/Email	

NOTES

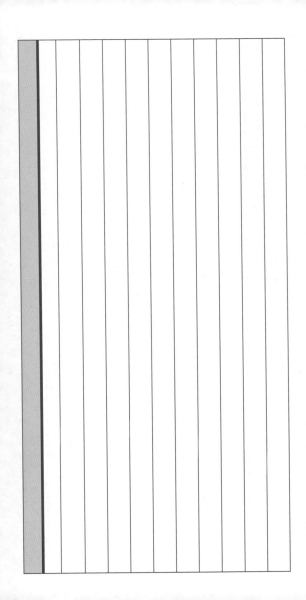

NOTES

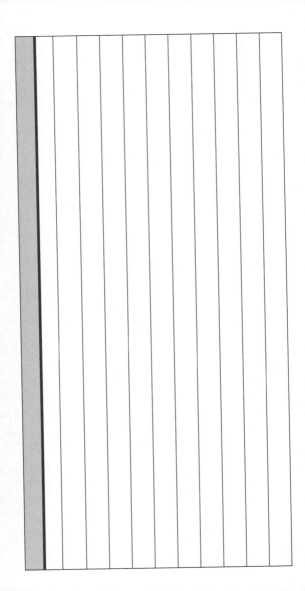

NOTES

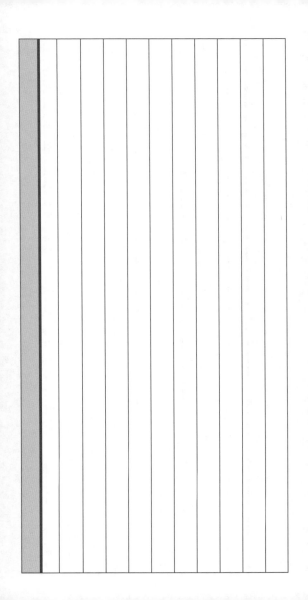

NOTES

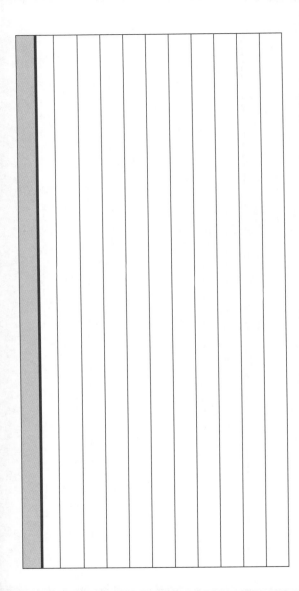

NOTES

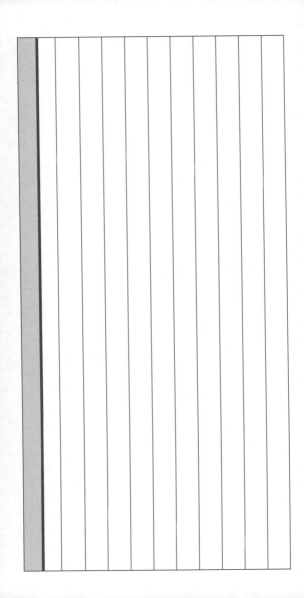

YEAR PLANNER

January _____

_____

_____

_____

February _____

_____

_____

_____

March _____

_____

_____

_____

April _____

_____

_____

_____

May _____

_____

_____

_____

June _____

_____

_____

_____